H

A GUIDE
TO VOLUNTARY WORK
IN IRELAND

This publication has been assisted by
AER LINGUS, BANK OF IRELAND and
GUINNESS IRELAND LTD.
and the support and encouragement received from
all the voluntary organisations who took the
time to respond to our questionnaires.

Aer Lingus ☘

HEY YOU!

A GUIDE
TO VOLUNTARY WORK
IN IRELAND

Researched and edited by
ANNE McGRATH and MARGARET COUGHLAN

WOLFHOUND PRESS

First published 1988 by
WOLFHOUND PRESS
68 Mountjoy Square,
Dublin 1.

British Library Cataloguing in Publication Data

McGrath, Anne
   Hey you! : a guide to voluntary work
   opportunities in Ireland — 2nd ed.
   1. Voluntary social services : Ireland.
   Directories
   I. Title   II. Coughlan, Margaret
   361.7′025′415

   ISBN 0-86327-172-3 pb

Cover design: Jan de Fouw
Typesetting: Redsetter Ltd., Dublin.
Printed and bound by the Leinster Leader Ltd., Naas.

INTRODUCTION

This second edition of *Hey You!* is the result of many hours of work by a great number of people. Questionnaires were sent out to over 200 organisations throughout Ireland during the past six months and the effort and interest shown by those who responded has been most encouraging. A small number did not wish to be included for various reasons and sadly many just did not reply despite numerous reminders.

There is a tremendous amount of work to be done in a variety of different ways and we have tried to separate the organisations into suitable categories in the Index. The one factor common to all is the need for fund-raising. This is not always specified but the statement by the Rape Crisis Centre – that voluntary assistance of just 4 hours flag day collecting is a very valuable contribution – could probably be repeated one hundred times over.

The voluntary work scene in Ireland has changed greatly since the first edition of *Hey You!* was published in 1978. Unfortunately some of the organisations included then have since had to close for various reasons. However several new ones have come into existence and now play a vital part in Irish society. A more recent trend is the 'self-help group' which offers support and information to people suffering from a particular disorder or their families and carers, by others who have had the same experience. These groups strictly speaking do not come under the heading of voluntary work but their members perform a very important and demanding role often while coping with their own difficult circumstances. We have included all the information we received from self-help groups and hope to research this area in more detail at a later date.

We hope that you the reader will find fulfilment in helping others through this book, and that the organisations listed will find the volunteers they all so badly need.

Margaret Coughlan
Anne McGrath

CONTENTS/INDEX

This index provides a general guide to the contents of this book. Many organisations listed cover more in practice than the single subject under which they might be indexed. The reader must refer to the entry proper to discover the scope of any organisation's activities. References are to entries, not to pages.

COMMUNITY WELFARE

COUNSELLING

DRUGS

HOMELESS

HOUSING

MARITAL

MENTAL DISABILITY

MENTAL HEALTH

PEACE & JUSTICE

PHYSICAL DISABILITY

SELF-HELP

THIRD WORLD

YOUTH

1. ACTION AID

Unity Buildings
16/17 Lr. O'Connell Street, Dublin 1. (01) 787911

NATURE OF WORK
Third World agency engaged in supporting individuals and communities through sponsorship. Volunteers are required for general office work, promotion, fundraising and development education of the agency's work for children especially in Northern Kenya.

VOLUNTEERS REQUIRED
Volunteers of all ages are welcome; office skills an advantage for assisting with office work.

TRAINING
Some basic training is given on the job.

HOURS
Office work by arrangement but between 9.15 to 17.30 Monday to Friday. Other work is usually done outside office hours.

CONTACT
Liam Flynn, Administrator, at above address.

2. ADAM AND EVE COUNSELLING AND CONSULTATION CENTRE

4 Merchants Quay, Dublin 8. (01) 711910/711245

NATURE OF WORK
Professional psychological and marital counselling assessment and training in preventative skills, funded by the Franciscan O.F.M. Order.

VOLUNTEERS REQUIRED
Volunteers must have at least an M.A. in psychology, completed and supervised Internship and be over forty years of age.

TRAINING
Postgraduate psychology students from U.C.D. have done an internship at this Centre.

HOURS
Clients are met by appointment between 9.30 a.m. and 5.30 p.m. Monday to Friday or by special arrangement after 5.30 p.m. and on Saturdays.

CONTACT
The above address during office hours.

3.   AFRI:
ACTION FROM IRELAND

P.O. Box 1522,
68 Mountjoy Square, Dublin 1. (01) 786755/786896

NATURE OF WORK
Working for Peace, Justice and Human Rights in Ireland
and the Third World.

VOLUNTEERS REQUIRED
Volunteers of all age groups are welcome, and required
usually at busy times rather than on a regular basis.
Office experience, particularly typing, is useful, but
there is a lot of work which everyone can do.

TRAINING
There is no training necessary as volunteers are required
for office duties and preparing mail shots, etc.

HOURS
By arrangement during office hours, 10 a.m. to 5.30 p.m.
Monday to Friday.

CONTACT
Orla at the above address during office hours.

4. AGENCY FOR PERSONAL SERVICE OVERSEAS (APSO)

29 Fitzwilliam Square, Dublin 2. (01) 614411

NATURE OF WORK

Funding of personal service overseas with Irish and international voluntary organisations and overseas governments. Training of development workers prior to departure to ensure that they are fully prepared for work overseas. Matching of people wishing to work overseas with suitable assignments available through Irish development agencies, APSO and European and International agencies, through the Agency's Overseas Register. Protection of interests of development workers in areas such as social welfare entitlements, superannuation, leave of absence and incremental credits.

VOLUNTEERS REQUIRED

Volunteers for overseas work must have qualifications, e.g. Mechanics, Doctors, Teachers, Carpenters, etc., and must be over 21 years of age.

TRAINING

Training programme includes courses on orientation for the development process and local environment, communications skills, particular professional skills and languages.

HOURS
Not applicable as this Agency is involved only with volunteers travelling overseas.

CONTACT
APSO Overseas Register, 29 Fitzwilliam Square, Dublin 2.

5.   ALCOHOLICS ANONYMOUS

109 South Circular Road,
Leonards Corner, Dublin 8. (01) 538998

NATURE OF WORK
A worldwide fellowship of men and women who help each other with recovery from alcoholism.

CONTACT
Full details of branches and meeting times are available from the above address.

6.   ALONE

3 Canal Terrace, Bluebell, Dublin 12. (01) 509614

NATURE OF WORK
Voluntary visitation of old people especially those who live alone and in derelict circumstances. The A.L.O.N.E. Organisation (A Little Offering Never Ends) was founded in 1977 by Willie Bermingham to expose and to help remedy the appalling conditions in which many isolated old are trapped and to encourage direct intervention by neighbours and relatives where the forgotten old suffer distress.

VOLUNTEERS REQUIRED
All volunteers are welcome, especially those who are sympathetic, good listeners and patient.

TRAINING
No training is necessary.

HOURS
Volunteers work approximately two or three hours each week.

CONTACT
The ALONE office, 3 Canal Terrace, Bluebell, Dublin 12.

7. THE ALZHEIMER SOCIETY OF IRELAND

St. John of God Hospital,
Stillorgan, Co. Dublin. (01) 881282

NATURE OF WORK
The care of patients suffering from Alzheimer's disease and related disorders and helping those who care for them.

VOLUNTEERS REQUIRED
25 years of age upwards, preferably with some experience in the nursing areas but this is not essential. Volunteers are required at present to help, on a rota basis, at Day Centres at Blackrock and Sandymount.

TRAINING
As the work is of a 'caring' nature training is not essential.

HOURS
11 a.m. to 4.30 p.m. at Day Centres on day or days of the volunteer's choice.

CONTACT
The Alzheimer Society of Ireland at the above address. Information may also be obtained here on the disease, and on venues and meeting times of support groups for carers, families and friends.

8.   ANKYLOSING SPONDYLITIS ASSOCIATION OF IRELAND

'Belpark', Elm Castle Drive,
Kilnamanagh, Dublin 24.

NATURE OF WORK
An association for sufferers of this disease to assist with the provision of information leaflets, meetings, and physiotherapy sessions.

CONTACT
Write to the Secretary, A.S.A.I. at the above address.

9.   ASSOCIATION FOR THE WELFARE OF CHILDREN IN HOSPITAL

1 Rock Lodge, Killiney, Co. Dublin.
(01) 851660/809520

NATURE OF WORK
A voluntary organisation seeking to increase the awareness of the public, medical personnel, hospital staffs, etc., of the special needs of child patients, and offering support and help to parents before during and after their child's stay in hospital. Volunteers are required for secretarial work, assisting with hospital playgroups, fund-raising, driving, or providing accommodation to parents near hospitals.

VOLUNTEERS REQUIRED
All volunteers are welcome but especially people who are good with children for playgroups and visiting.

TRAINING
The association provides workshops in Dublin and evening lectures for volunteers.

HOURS
Playgroups are usually for about two hours in the mornings. All other work is by arrangement.

CONTACT
The National Executive at the above address or branches at:

Dublin: c/o 148 Beechpark, Lucan. (01) 241066
Cork: c/o 11 The Crescent, Gardiner's Hill. (021) 501534
Galway: c/o 3 Devon Gardens, Salthill. (091) 23482
Limerick: c/o 30 Meadowvale, Raheen. (061) 28716
Wexford: c/o Riverside, Crosstown. (053) 24875

10. ASTHMA SOCIETY OF IRELAND

24 Anglesea Street, Dublin 2. (01) 716551

NATURE OF WORK
An association of asthmatics and parents of asthmatic children providing support and information, organising annual holidays for asthmatic children and other functions.

VOLUNTEERS REQUIRED
Volunteers with office experience are required to assist with the Asthma Information Service. Residential helpers with experience of working with children aged 8 – 13 are needed for the annual 6-day holiday in August.

TRAINING
All volunteers receive on the job training.

HOURS
Office work is by arrangement during office hours. Holidays are live-in for one week in August, Sunday to Saturday.

CONTACT
Orán O'Muire, Administrator, at above address.

11. BARNARDO'S

244 Harold's Cross Road, Dublin 6.
(01) 977313/977276

NATURE OF WORK
Child care and social work providing Day Nurseries, Toy Libraries, Adoption Advice and other services. Volunteers are required for fund-raising and to assist the trained child care staff.

VOLUNTEERS REQUIRED
Volunteers must be over 18 years of age.

TRAINING
Where appropriate training is given relevant to the work undertaken.

HOURS
Minimum two or three hours per week between 10.00 a.m. and 4.00 p.m. Monday to Friday, but hours can vary according to need.

CONTACT
Apply in writing to the Director, Barnardo's, 244 Harold's Cross Road, Dublin 6.

SHARE YOUR HEALTH
PLEASE GIVE BLOOD

PELICAN HOUSE CLINIC TIMES		
	Mondays	9.30 am - 8.15 pm
	Tuesdays	9.30 am - 8.15 pm
	Wednesdays	9.30 am - 4.15 pm
	Thursdays	9.30 am - 4.15 pm
	Fridays	9.30 am - 4.15 pm
		Including lunchtime.
REGIONAL CENTRE CLINIC TIMES	Mondays	11.30 am - 2.30 pm including lunchtime
	Thursdays	5.00 pm - 8.00 pm
	Fridays	10.00 am - 12.30 pm

SEE LOCAL CLINIC NOTICES FOR DETAILS OF MOBILE UNIT VISITS

The Blood Transfusion Service Board

Pelican House, 40 Mespil Road, Dublin 4 (01) 603333
Regional Centre, AT St Finbarr's Hospital, Douglas Road, Cork (021) 968799

12. THE BLOOD TRANSFUSION SERVICE BOARD

Pelican House, P.O. Box 97,
40 Mespil Road, Dublin 4. (01) 603333

NATURE OF WORK

The functions of the Blood Transfusion Service Board include the organisation and administration of a blood transfusion service including the processing or supply of blood derivatives or other blood products.

VOLUNTEERS REQUIRED

The volunteers required by the Board are blood donors and plasma donors. Donors must be aged between 18 and 65 with a minimum weight of 50 kg (8 stone approx.) and in normal health with no history of infectious hepatitis (jaundice). New donors are always needed to provide for the ever expanding requirements of modern medical care. In addition, the plasmapheresis programme, a donation technique where plasma is separated from the blood while the donation is proceeding, requires another new group of donors. This product is needed for the successful treatment of haemophilia and other blood-clotting disorders and to lessen our dependence upon imported blood products.

HOURS

Blood donor clinic times are set out in the attached ad. Plasma clinics are open Monday to Friday 9.30 – 4 p.m. and an appointment is required.

CONTACT
Pelican House as above, or the Regional Centre at St. Finbarr's Hospital, Douglas Road, Cork. (021) 968799.

13.   CAIRDE

Halfpenny Court,
36 Lr. Ormond Quay, Dublin 1. (01) 733799/730877

NATURE OF WORK
Cairde is a supporting/helping voluntary group for people affected by AIDS, regardless of race, religion or sexual preference. Cairde means 'Friends', and Cairde volunteers become friends/buddies of the AIDS affected person, while there are professional counsellors involved who are available to provide counselling if requested.

VOLUNTEERS REQUIRED
Minimum age 18. There are no specific qualifications required but volunteers would need to be reasonably together, sensible, and willing to learn.

TRAINING
There is an interview system for prospective volunteers and an initial comprehensive training weekend with ongoing training programmes and support group meetings every two weeks.

HOURS
Minimum of two hours every two weeks. Hours would obviously increase as befriending occurs.

CONTACT
The Recruitment Officer at:
Halfpenny Court, 36 Lr. Ormond Quay, Dublin 1.
20 Upper Dominick Street, Galway.
22 Mac Curtain Street, Cork.

14.   CANDLE COMMUNITY TRUST

P.O. Box 1145, Kylemore Road,
Rear Church of the Assumption, Ballyfermot,
Dublin 10. (01) 269111/2

NATURE OF WORK
Candle is involved in working with young men of 15 years and upwards in the Ballyfermot area, operating a day centre and training workshop. They aim to facilitate the potential for growth and development through building relationships and offering friendship, advice and support. Training in the skills of metal work and wood work are provided through the workshop and the day centre offers recreational activities and education in an informal sense. A full-time staff and part-time teachers are employed but voluntary leaders play an important role in the day centre activities.

VOLUNTEERS REQUIRED
No qualifications are necessary but volunteers should be over 18 with an ability to relate and understand young people. They should have an open non-judgmental attitude and be willing to learn and share their experience of life.

TRAINING
No formal training is given but regular meetings are held to facilitate leaders.

HOURS
The day centre is open three nights a week and hours are flexible but volunteers are expected to work at least two hours a week.

CONTACT
Mr. Joe Wallace, Director, at the above address.

15. CARE FOR DUBLIN'S OLD FOLK LIVING ALONE

c/o Welfare Section, Capel Buildings,
68-72 Gt. Strand Street, Dublin 1.

NATURE OF WORK
Regular visits to the old and needy living alone in all areas of Dublin, and helping to subsidise their income by giving food parcels, coal and clothing where necessary.

VOLUNTEERS REQUIRED
Volunteers should be over 18 with a genuine interest in the aged and their welfare and an ability to respect the confidential nature of the work.

TRAINING
Volunteers are introduced to the work and receive ongoing support and guidance.

HOURS
Members work in their spare time for at least one or two hours a week.

CONTACT
Ms. Eileen Coen, Hon. Secretary, at above address.

16.   C.A.S.A. CARING AND SHARING ASSOCIATION

Administration Centre,
10 Upper Leeson Stret, Dublin 4. (01) 681998/602669

NATURE OF WORK
CASA is an organisation of voluntary helpers and handicapped people, usually on a one-to-one balance, aiming to build genuine friendship and develop awareness between handicapped and helper members through activities such as outings, social evenings, holidays, pilgrimages and fundraising.

VOLUNTEERS REQUIRED
Helpers should be willing and interested and prepared to make a commitment to the Group. There are no set age limits but preferably volunteers should be   mature teenagers and upwards.

TRAINING
New helpers are encouraged to join in all the activities under the supervision of a leader or experienced helper.

HOURS
Meetings and Evening Socials take one night each week; Sunday socials and outings approx. one Sunday a month. A 24-hour commitment is required of helpers on one-week holidays and mini-holidays and at the organisation's Break-House in Drumcondra, Dublin.

CONTACT
There are at present 28 groups in existence throughout Ireland. Full details can be obtained from the Administration Centre as above, or c/o The Annex, Good Shepherd Convent, Sundays Well, Cork.

17. CATHOLIC MARRIAGE ADVISORY COUNCIL

All Hallows College,
Drumcondra, Dublin 9. (01) 371151

NATURE OF WORK
Marriage counselling and pre-marriage courses. Volunteers are required as counsellors and to help with office work and administration.

VOLUNTEERS REQUIRED
Counsellors and host couples for pre-marriage courses should be over 25 and some years married.

TRAINING
All volunteers receive adequate training for the work undertaken.

n courses and local branch arrange-

ral branches throughout Ireland whose
opening hours are listed in the telephone
ll details may also be obtained from the
e, CMAC, c/o All Hallows College,
Drumcondra, Dublin 9.

18.   CATHOLIC YOUTH COUNCIL

20/23 Arran Quay, Dublin 7. (01) 725055

NATURE OF WORK
CYC supports and services youth ministry and youth
work in the Archdiocese of Dublin. Services include
Youth Clubs, Summer Projects, Training and Education,
Competitions and Events, Faith Development, Residen-
tial Centres and Information.

VOLUNTEERS REQUIRED
Volunteers over 18 years of age are often required to
work with young people in Youth Clubs/Groups, and in
the organisation and running of Summer Projects.

TRAINING
Relevant training is provided for volunteers where
necessary.

HOURS
Volunteers mostly work evenings and weekends. During Summer Projects volunteers may be required to do some work during the day.

CONTACT
Contact your local Youth Club/Group or your local Summer Project Committee. For addresses or other information contact C.Y.C. Headquarters at above address or Regional Offices at:

19 Quinsboro Road, Bray, Co. Wicklow. (01) 828324

V.E.C. Offices, Eblana Avenue, Dun Laoghaire,
    Co. Dublin. (01) 800386

c/o St. Joseph's B.N.S., Boot Road, Clondalkin,
    Dublin 12. (01) 572666

85 Main Street, Swords, Co. Dublin. (01) 405100

Neilstown/Rowlagh Resource Centre, Neilstown,
    Dublin 22. (01) 570849

19.   CENTRAL REMEDIAL CLINIC

Vernon Avenue, Clontarf, Dublin 3. (01) 332206

NATURE OF WORK
National centre for children, adolescents and adults with physical and multiple handicaps providing a broad range of medical and support services.

VOLUNTEERS REQUIRED
There are over 100 volunteers involved with the Clinic on a wide variety of tasks. Anyone between the ages of 16 and 65 is welcome but particularly those who are good at

crafts or have experience in the caring profession or teaching.

TRAINING
Applicants fill in an application form and are interviewed before selection. On the job training and special training sessions are provided where appropriate.

HOURS
Hours are by arrangement and very flexible – full-time, two or three days, or a couple of hours a week, permanent, short-term, or even on call.

CONTACT
Emer Ingoldsby, Development Officer, at the above address.

20. CENTRECARE

1A Cathedral Street, Dublin 1. (01) 745441

NATURE OF WORK
Centrecare is a Diocesan social service centre within the precincts of the Pro-Cathedral and offering a professional counselling and support service in many areas including personal problems, relationship, accommodation and spiritual problems.

VOLUNTEERS REQUIRED
Volunteers are required to assist the professional staff in reception work and possibly in other areas of work in the future.

TRAINING
Training is provided for volunteers.

HOURS
Volunteers' hours are by arrangement and flexible. The Centre is open daily from 9 a.m. to 6 p.m. Monday to Saturday.

CONTACT
The social worker on duty at the above address.

21. CEREBRAL PALSY IRELAND

Sandymount Avenue, Dublin 4. (01) 695355

NATURE OF WORK
CPI CENTRES provide services for physically disabled children and adults which include pre-schools, special national schools, clinics, workshops, sport and leisure activities.
CPI BRANCHES provide support groups for people with cerebral palsy and parents of children with cerebral palsy.

VOLUNTEERS REQUIRED
Mature men and women are required to assist professional staff, help maintain centres and as drivers.

TRAINING
Simple training is provided in certain specialist fields.

HOURS
Work in centres is usually on weekdays during school hours, sports and leisure activities are usually in the evenings or at weekends. Branches hold monthly evening meetings and special projects.

CONTACT
Contact the Superintendent, CPI Centre:
Cork Spastic Clinic, Ballintemple, Cork. (021) 294803
Marino Clinic, Church Road, Bray, Co. Wicklow.
　(01) 867543
O'Neill Centre, St. Joseph's Road, Kilkenny. (056) 62326
Sandymount Centre, Sandymount Avenue, Dublin 4.
　(01) 695355
Cerebral Palsy Sport, c/o Sandymount Centre.
There are over twenty branches throughout Ireland and a list of Branch Secretaries is available from Headquarters as above.

22.　CHERISH

2 Lr. Pembroke Street, Dublin 2. (01) 682744

NATURE OF WORK
A professional counselling and support service to single parents, Cherish only recruits volunteers for fund-raising events.

VOLUNTEERS REQUIRED
Anyone interested in assisting with fund-raising is welcome.

TRAINING
No training is required.

HOURS
Hours depend on fund-raising activity undertaken.

CONTACT
The Administrator at the above address.
Details of membership and meetings, etc., are also available from this address.

23.   THE CHESHIRE FOUNDATION IN IRELAND

20A Herbert Lane, Dublin 2. (01) 614550

NATURE OF WORK
Providing residential care for adults with severe physical disabilities through the seven Cheshire Homes located throughout the country. The homes aim to enable the residents to live as full and meaningful a life as possible in a homely, rather than institutional setting.

VOLUNTEERS REQUIRED
Anyone who can offer a service is welcome and there are many ways to help, such as organising outings and entertainments for the residents, fund-raising, or by simply listening. Persons with qualifications in any of the arts, Yoga, etc. could be very beneficial.

TRAINING
Training varies from Home to Home but usually there

would be a general introductory talk from the Head of the Home.

HOURS
Hours are flexible and would depend on the individual's availability and the voluntary tasks undertaken.

CONTACT
Mark Blake-Knox, Cheshire Foundation in Ireland, at the above address, or the Head of Home or Administrator in each of the Homes as follows:

Ardeen Cheshire Home, Shillelagh, Co. Wicklow.
Barrett Cheshire Home, 21 Herbert Street, Dublin 2.
Cara Cheshire Home, Phoenix Park, Chapelizod,
    Dublin 20.
O'Dwyer Cheshire Home, Bohola, Lismirrane,
    Swinford, Co. Mayo.
Rathfredagh Cheshire Home, Newcastle West,
    Co. Limerick.
St. Laurence Cheshire Home, Lota Park, Cork.
St. Patrick's Cheshire Home, Tullow, Co. Carlow.
There are also plans for new Cheshire Homes in Galway, Monkstown Co. Dublin, and Donegal.

24. CHILDRENS LEUKAEMIA RESEARCH PROJECT

40 Clancy Avenue, Finglas East,
Dublin 11. (01) 343986

NATURE OF WORK
A voluntary Fund-raising and support group for parents

and friends of children with leukaemia.

VOLUNTEERS REQUIRED
Persons over 18 years with a real interest in the work are always welcome.

TRAINING
Basic training is provided relevant to the work undertaken.

HOURS
This would depend on the event being organised at the time.

CONTACT
Ray McCormack, Secretary, at the above address.

25 CIVIL DEFENCE

Civil Defence Branch, Colaiste Caoimhin, Glasnevin, Dublin 9. (01) 379911

NATURE OF WORK
Civil Defence is established as part of the National Defence structure principally to provide for the protection of the civil population in wartime; the organisation can also be employed to assist in peacetime disasters or emergencies.

VOLUNTEERS REQUIRED
No specific qualifications are required and anyone over the age of seventeen can apply to join Civil Defence.

TRAINING
Volunteers are trained on a weekly basis in specific skills. Civil Defence has five main services – Rescue, Casualty, Welfare, Auxiliary Fire Service and Warden Service.

HOURS
Volunteers will be called out in specific emergencies but training exercises are held regularly at times arranged locally. This training is supplemented by exercises, field-days, week-end camps and other activities designed to give volunteers an opportunity to put into practical use the skills and knowledge which they have acquired in training.

CONTACT
Civil Defence is a national organisation with Civil Defence officers in every county. Local initiatives in recruiting are supported by periodic national publicity campaigns. For full details contact headquarters as above.

26   COELIAC SOCIETY OF IRELAND

32 Clyde Road, Dublin 4. (01) 683399

NATURE OF WORK
Promoting and protecting the interests of Coeliacs in Ireland by advising on gluten-free diets, organising cookery demonstrations, providing literature, etc.

VOLUNTEERS REQUIRED
Volunteers of all age groups, men and women, are welcome. No specific qualifications are required, just a genuine interest in the condition.

TRAINING
No particular training is needed.

HOURS
Hours are not specific but volunteers should be available for meetings and helping in the Society's activities.

CONTACT
The National Secretary at the above address.

27 COMFORT FOR CANCER

'Allendale', 5 Summerhill Road,
Sandycove, Co. Dublin. (01) 806505

NATURE OF WORK
To give comfort to those touced by the illness of cancer by holding meetings to share common experiences, meeting socially, corresponding with and telephoning one another.

VOLUNTEERS REQUIRED
This support group is open to all cancer patients, their families and/or friends.

TRAINING
No training is required.

HOURS
Support group meets on the 1st Friday of the month at 7.30 in St. Ann's Church, Dawson Street, Dublin 2.

CONTACT
Full details from the above address.

28 CONCERN

1 Upper Camden Street, Dublin 2. (01) 681237

NATURE OF WORK
Concern is a Third World Agency involved in the operation of projects in the least developed countries, raising funds to support these projects, and increasing public awareness of world poverty.

VOLUNTEERS REQUIRED
For overseas work volunteers must have a profession such as nursing, agriculture, social work, engineering or management. Volunteers at home are required mainly to assist local groups by undertaking a fast for 48 hours at Christmas time.

TRAINING
Volunteers for overseas work receive training and support.

HOURS
Hours by arrangement depending on work undertaken.

CONTACT

For overseas work contact the Overseas Dept. and for home work the Concern Development Dept. both at 1 Upper Camden Street, Dublin 2.

29 CONSUMERS' ASSOCIATION OF IRELAND LTD.

45 Upper Mount Street, Dublin 2. (01) 612466

NATURE OF WORK

Consumer information and protection.

VOLUNTEERS REQUIRED

On occasion volunteers are sought for small-scale research, campaign lobbying, and for the association's Advice and Information Service. Qualifications help but are not necessary. Interest and determination are important.

TRAINING

Training varies depending on the work involved.

HOURS

There are no fixed hours and flexibility is important.

CONTACT

Write to May McLoughlin, Administrator, at the above address.

30 COOLMINE THERAPEUTIC COMMUNITY

Coolmine House,
19 Lord Edward Street, Dublin 2. (01) 782300

NATURE OF WORK
Residential drug addict rehabilitation. This group also provides AIDS education and prevention advice, a Drug Prevention Programme for parishes or parent groups, a Family Resource Centre and Evening Groups, and a non-residential Day Programme.

VOLUNTEERS REQUIRED
Volunteers must be over 21 years.

TRAINING
Suitable training is given to all volunteers.

HOURS
Hours are arranged individually.

CONTACT
Tom McGarry, Programme Director, at the above address.

31 COPING WITH GRIEF

Magheraboy, Carrickmacross, Co. Monaghan.

NATURE OF WORK
A self-help group to help the newly bereaved to cope

with their grief for as long as is necessary or those who
need to grieve.

VOLUNTEERS REQUIRED
Two or more people who have successfully coped with
their own grief are required as leaders for each group to
organise and run meetings.

TRAINING
Leaders receive initial training and there is an on-going
professional back-up available.

HOURS
Groups usually meet for about two hours each month by
local arrangement.

CONTACT
There are approximately eight groups throughout the
country and details are available by sending enquiries
and s.a.e. to the Head Office, Magheraboy, Carrickmacross, Co. Monaghan, or to 24 Lr. Rathmines Road, Dublin
6. (01) 962201

32 THE CORK & DISTRICT
AMPUTEES ASSOCIATION

c/o The Moorings, Doughcloyne, Cork.

NATURE OF WORK
A voluntary group working to improve the service for
amputees. New amputees are referred by the local

Orthopaedic Hospital and members offer information, support and advice.

CONTACT
For full details write to the above address.

33 CORK MENTAL WELFARE ASSOCIATION

St. Rita's Rehabilitation Centre,
Lee Road, Cork. (021) 543793

NATURE OF WORK
Rehabilitation of the mentally ill through workshops and hostels.

VOLUNTEERS REQUIRED
Volunteers should be over 18 with an interest in the mentally ill.

TRAINING
No training is given.

HOURS
Hours are by arrangement and depend on the work undertaken.

CONTACT
Mrs. N. Jennings, Secretary, at the above address.

34   CUAN MHUIRE REHABILITATION CENTRE

Athy, Co. Kildare. (0507) 31493

NATURE OF WORK
Rehabilitation of Alcoholics. Founded by Sr. Consilio, Cuan Mhuire centres care for alcoholics mentally, physically and medically in an atmosphere of openness and love, hope and motivation.

VOLUNTEERS REQUIRED
Any volunteers are very welcome at any time, whether qualified or not.

TRAINING
Volunteers work with staff initially.

HOURS
Hours are dependent on the type of work but never for more than four or five hours in one day.

CONTACT
There are now three Cuan Mhuire centres, all autonomous under the direction of Sr. Consilio. Contacts are as follows:
Sr. Helen, Cuan Mhuire, Athy, Co. Kildare.
Sr. Agnes, Cuan Mhuire, Bruree, Co. Limerick.
Sr. Consilio, Cuan Mhuire, Newry, Co. Down.

35 CYSTIC FIBROSIS ASSOCIATION OF IRELAND

C.F. House,
24 Lower Rathmines Road, Dublin 6. (01) 962433

NATURE OF WORK
An organisation of support and help for patients and parents of those suffering with Cystic Fibrosis.

VOLUNTEERS REQUIRED
All interested persons and fund-raisers are welcome and should be over 14 years.

TRAINING
Adequate training is given to all volunteers.

HOURS
Volunteers work in their own time by arrangement.

CONTACT
The National Officer at the above address.

36 THE DOM MARMION SOCIETY

c/o Holy Cross Church, Dundrum, Dublin 14.
(01) 982814

NATURE OF WORK
Care of the Elderly and Lonely.

VOLUNTEERS REQUIRED
All volunteers who are interested in this kind of work are welcome.

TRAINING
No official training is given.

HOURS
Volunteers work by arrangement in their own time.

CONTACT
Carmel Whelan, 17 Annaville Park, Dundrum, Dublin 14. (01) 982814

37 DR. TOM DOOLEY FUND

47 Fitzwilliam Square, Dublin 2.

NATURE OF WORK
An agency for sending nurses overseas to work in the Third World.

VOLUNTEERS REQUIRED
All volunteers must be qualified nurses or midwives.

TRAINING
Volunteers are trained by APSO (see entry No. 4).

HOURS
Volunteers work in the Third World under contract for two years.

CONTACT
Details can be obtained by writing to any of the follow-ing:
Dr. Barnes, 47 Fitzwilliam Square, Dublin 2.
Peggy Henry, Treasurer, Cuala, Greenfield Road,
    Sutton, Co. Dublin.
Denise Whelan, Secretary, c/o Beaumont Hospital,
    Dublin 9.

38   DUBLIN CENTRAL MISSION

Marlborough Place, Dublin 1. (01) 742123

NATURE OF WORK
A Social Aid Centre providing various services such as a
Coffee Bar for Alcoholics; a Halfway House; Housing for
Elderly Persons; a Clothes Shop; General pastoral
Support; the Olive Grove Coffee & Snack Bar.

VOLUNTEERS REQUIRED
Volunteers are required for friendship work in the
evenings at the Halfway House and must be over 20
years of age with a genuine care for people and a willing-ness to listen regularly. Help is also needed for flag day
collecting and serving in the Coffee Bar.

TRAINING
No specific training is given to volunteers.

HOURS
Volunteers in the Halfway House work in the evening
for a few hours weekly; Flag days are once a year at the

end of November; Volunteers in the Coffee Bar work a few hours daytime each week.

CONTACT
Halfway House: Sister Alice Musgrave.
Flag Days: Mrs. Irene Galloway.
Coffee Bar: Mr. Graham Caswell.
– all at the Social Aid Centre, Marlborough Place, Dublin 1.

39   ENDOMETRIOSIS SOCIETY OF IRELAND

c/o Foxlease, Stonehall, Ballisodare, Co. Sligo.

NATURE OF WORK
A self-help group of sufferers aiming to increase awareness of the disease and to encourage and support research.

HOURS
Members meet on the first Saturday of every month at the Cherish premises, 2 Lr. Pembroke Street, Dublin 2.

CONTACT
Mrs. Mildred Gilmore at the above address, (071) 67353, evenings and weekends only, or Mrs. Regina Buckley, 'Birdhurst', 10 Nutley Park, Donnybrook, Dublin 4.

40 FAMILY RESOURCE CENTRE

St. Vincents,
North William Street, Dublin 1. (01) 788249

NATURE OF WORK
The Centre offers support and intensive work to families who are in crisis including single parents, separated parents, travellers, drug addicts, and mothers with a psychiatric condition. The aim is to keep the family together during the crisis. The children referred are from birth up to 6 years with a range of problems, i.e. emotionally disturbed, mentally handicapped, behavioural problems, developmental delay.

VOLUNTEERS REQUIRED
Volunteers are required to assist the professional staff in the Centre and on home visits and must be over 18 years, preferably with some child care/pre-school training experience.

TRAINING
Volunteers would be guided into the work but would never be given total responsibility for any child or family.

HOURS
This would be entirely up to the volunteers.

CONTACT
Sr. Cecilia Walsh at the above address.

41   FOCUS POINT

14A-15 Eustace Street, Dublin 2. (01) 776421/718086

NATURE OF WORK

Focus Point is a self-help resource centre for people who are out-of-home or who have severe accommodation problems. The agency helps settle people into the community in housing suitable to their needs by providing information, advice and counselling, a 24-hour phone service, a settlement service, Outreach street-work, Drop-In centres, creche facilities and restaurant, Houses of Hospitality, educational resources and research.

VOLUNTEERS REQUIRED

Volunteers are required to assist in various project work: Fund-raise for the agency; Become aware of and inform people of the situation of homeless people in Ireland.

TRAINING

Adequate training is given for the work undertaken.

HOURS

Hours are variable depending on the type of work.

CONTACT

Volunteers are required to fill out an application form and should write to Eilis Fitzgerald at Focus Point National Headquarters as above.

42   FRIENDS OF THE ELDERLY

7 Charlemont Street, Dublin 2. (01) 755500/757818

NATURE OF WORK
Working to alleviate loneliness and social isolation among elderly people. Services include home visiting; hospital visiting; club; outings and parties; holidays; home improvements and transport. The Friends also provide advice and information to elderly people and advocate on their behalf, as necessary.

VOLUNTEERS REQUIRED
Volunteers living in or near Dublin 1, 2, 4, 6, 8, 12. Volunteer drivers living in any areas, particularly people who could do some driving jobs during the day. Volunteers are asked to give a one year commitment to the organisation.

TRAINING
All new volunteers attend a half-day introductory seminar and occasional training programmes are held involving a series of 6-8 talks.

HOURS
Hours are flexible and by arrangement with the volunteers.

CONTACT
Contact Friends of the Elderly at the above address.

43   GINGERBREAD IRELAND

12 Wicklow Street, Dublin 2. (01) 710291

NATURE OF WORK
A self-help group for parents bringing up children on their own, and providing an Information Centre, Legal Advice Clinic, counselling and mediation, and creche child care facilities for members children.

VOLUNTEERS REQUIRED
Assistants of any age are required for typing and general office duties and for fund-raising.

TRAINING
The Information Centre is run from the office in Wicklow Street and training is given in Welfare rights, etc. Volunteers are also encouraged to do some training in non-directive counselling.

HOURS
The Information Centre is open Monday to Friday 10 a.m. to 5 p.m. and volunteers work a rota system within these hours.

CONTACT
Telephone the Information Centre at 710291 during office hours.

44 GLENCREE CENTRE FOR RECONCILIATION

Enniskerry, Bray, Co. Wicklow. (01) 860963

NATURE OF WORK
Reconciliation work focusing on programmes aimed at young people in such areas as environmental studies, North/South exchanges, youth encounter weekends, farm education for young children and international workcamps.

VOLUNTEERS REQUIRED
International and Irish volunteers are welcome, minimum age 20 years. Prior experience or a keen interest in community living is an asset as community life is a strong and vital part of Glencree.

TRAINING
Informal training is given in such areas as listening skills, communication skills, conflict management skills, and facilitation.

HOURS
Full-time volunteers serve either a one year term or three months in Summer. As members of a community volunteers live in the Centre where each volunteer is given areas of responsibilities. Hours are flexible with a 6-day work week, one week-end off a month and three weeks off a year.

CONTACT
Gloria Fralick, Co-ordinator, at the above address.

45 GOAL

P.O. Box 19, Dun Laoghaire, Co. Dublin. (01) 809779

NATURE OF WORK
Famine relief and Third World development mainly in the medical sector.

VOLUNTEERS REQUIRED
Registered general nurses and midwives, doctors, administrators, accountants, engineers and mechanics.

TRAINING
Volunteers are required to attend training courses given by the Agency for Personnel Services Overseas, 29 Fitzwilliam Square, Dublin 2. (See entry No. 4).

HOURS
Depend on the programme in question.

CONTACT
John O'Shea, Maeve Long or Mary White at 809779.

46 GORTA

12 Herbert Street, Dublin 2. (01) 615522

NATURE OF WORK
Agricultural development in Third World countries.

VOLUNTEERS REQUIRED
Volunteers must have either a degree or diploma in

Agriculture, Horticulture, Home Economics or Veterinary Medicine.

TRAINING
All volunteers must attend courses organised by APSO. (See entry No. 4).

CONTACT
Applicants with suitable qualifications should write to Gorta at the above address.

47   GROW

National Centre, 11 Liberty Street, Cork.
(021) 506520

NATURE OF WORK
A community mental health movement. Through its programme, group method and caring community Grow shows one how to make full use of personal resources in overcoming inadequacies and maladjustments and growing to personal maturity.

VOLUNTEERS REQUIRED
People aged 18 years and upwards are needed to lead groups. The only requirements are a willingness to grow with others towards maturity and a caring heart.

TRAINING
Training sessions are provided for leaders.

HOURS
Volunteers are required for two hours per week and to attend a two-hour monthly meeting.

CONTACT
Contact should be made during office hours to the National Centre as above, or Regional Offices:
35 Parliament Street, Kilkenny. (056) 61624
58 Middle Abbey Street, Dublin 1. (01) 734029

48   THE HANLY CENTRE

The Mews, Eblana Avenue, Dun Laoghaire,
Co. Dublin. (01) 809795/807269

NATURE OF WORK
Confidential information and counselling service for those whose lives – either personally or indirectly – are affected by a drinking problem, through Education Programmes, Lecture/Discussion Courses, Group Therapy, Rebuilding Resources, etc.

VOLUNTEERS REQUIRED
Volunteers are required from time to time to assist with telephone and reception work.

TRAINING
A general introduction to the work of the Centre and on the job training is provided.

HOURS
Volunteers work by arrangement during office hours, 10

a.m. – 1 p.m. or 1.45 – 4 p.m.

CONTACT
Odette Thompson or Kay Duffy at the above address.

49 HYPERACTIVE CHILDRENS SUPPORT GROUP IRELAND

4 Elton Park, Sandycove, Co. Dublin. (01) 808766

NATURE OF WORK
The group helps and supports hyperactive children and their parents; conducts research and promotes investigation into the incidence of hyperactivity in Ireland, its causes and treatments; and disseminates information concerning this condition.

VOLUNTEERS REQUIRED
Men and women aged 18 years and upwards are required for secretarial and nursing duties.

TRAINING
No specific training is given to volunteers.

HOURS
Hours are by arrangement and flexible.

CONTACT
Phone Sarah Nichols as above, evenings only 8 p.m. to 10 p.m.

50   ILEOSTOMY ASSOCIATION OF G.B. & IRELAND

1 Woodfarm Avenue, Palmerstown, Dublin 20.
(01) 265355

NATURE OF WORK
An association of people who have experienced an ileostomy operation to help those who are about to have an operation to return to fully active life and to prove by example that it can be done. The association helps with all aspects of rehabilitation, social activities and relationships, and promotes and co-ordinates research.

VOLUNTEERS REQUIRED
Volunteers of all ages are required mainly for hospital and/or home visits.

TRAINING
All volunteers receive initial training.

HOURS
Hours are flexible and by arrangement.

CONTACT
Francis Scahill at the above address.

51   INCEST CRISIS SERVICE

P.O. Box 1543, Dublin 6. (01) 743796

NATURE OF WORK
Providing a crisis telephone line and individual, family

and group counselling for people who have been
sexually abused or closely affected by sexual abuse, and
providing information and advice on request about
sexual abuse and services available.

VOLUNTEERS REQUIRED
Volunteers are required to have had counselling training, e.g. qualified social workers, clinical psychologists
or trained volunteer counsellors.

TRAINING
Training is provided for volunteers.

HOURS
Hours are flexible according to volunteer interest and
time availability.

CONTACT
Write to the Co-ordinator, Incest Crisis Service, 30
Mountjoy Square, Dublin 1, or phone 743796.

52   INTERAID

27 Wyattville Close, Ballybrack, Co. Dublin.
(01) 825885

NATURE OF WORK
A voluntary housing organisation providing low-cost
interim accommodation for people in need of it. Small
flats or bedsitters are available in residential districts for
tenants, including handicapped and socially vulnerable
people, who need temporary accommodation and who

would have difficulty in finding and paying for private rented housing.

VOLUNTEERS REQUIRED
At present Interaid owns three houses in Dublin and volunteers are required to assist with house maintenance, collection and delivery of household furniture, and for fund-raising.

TRAINING
No training is necessary for the work involved.

HOURS
Whatever time is available to the individual.

CONTACT
Contact the Social Officer, Sally McFarlane, at the above address.

53   IRISH ASSOCIATION FOR SPINA BIFIDA AND HYDROCEPHALUS

Old Nangor Road, Clondalkin, Dublin 22.
(01) 572326

NATURE OF WORK
An association of parents and friends of children with Spina Bifida who require volunteers to assist with social, recreational and domestic activities on residential one-week holidays during the summer months. There are

approximately ten children in each group together with Nursing staff, Therapists and Volunteers.

VOLUNTEERS REQUIRED
House Parents, male and female, who must be over 21 years, and Voluntary Helpers aged 16 upwards.

TRAINING
Full orientation is provided before selections.

HOURS
Residential for one week – Saturday 11 a.m. to Saturday 11 a.m.

CONTACT
Miriam McSharry or Mary Darragh at the above address.

54 IRISH CANCER SOCIETY

5 Northumberland Road, Dublin 4. (01) 681855

NATURE OF WORK
Care of the terminally ill, Information and Education programmes, Provision of Hospital Equipment and Research.

VOLUNTEERS REQUIRED
Volunteers are required to assist with office, clerical and telephonist work.

TRAINING
Limited training is provided.

HOURS
Volunteers work by arrangement during office hours.

CONTACT
Mr. R. T. Hudson at the Dublin Headquarters as above, or the Cork office at 15 Bridge Street.

55   IRISH DIABETIC ASSOCIATION

82/83 Lr. Gardiner Street, Dublin 1. (01) 363022

NATURE OF WORK
To help Diabetics, particularly newly diagnosed, to understand their treatment, to provide a meeting place for Diabetics, to represent their interest, and to raise money for the support of the Association and for research.

VOLUNTEERS REQUIRED
Volunteers are required to assist with general administration and for fund-raising.

TRAINING
No training is required.

HOURS
Hours would depend on the work undertaken.

CONTACT
Branches have now been established in Donegal, Galway, Limerick, Mayo, Offaly, Tipperary, Wexford and Wicklow, and full details are available from the Dublin office as above.

56   IRISH EPILEPSY ASSOCIATION

249 Crumlin Road, Dublin 12. (01) 557500

NATURE OF WORK
To help and counsel people with epilepsy, their families
and friends.

VOLUNTEERS REQUIRED
Volunteers of all age groups and no particular qualifications are needed to assist the association in a variety of
ways.

TRAINING
Training will be provided if necessary.

HOURS
Hours depend on the type of work undertaken and the
commitment of the volunteer.

CONTACT
Geraldine Harney, Research & Development Officer, at
the above address.

57   IRISH HAEMOPHILIA SOCIETY

29 Eaton Square, Monkstown, Co. Dublin.

NATURE OF WORK
Creating a bond between members and the Society by
means of factsheets and link-line services, giving advice
and assistance to members, negotiating with authorities

on behalf of haemophiliacs and generally endeavouring to create an awareness nationally of haemophilia. To these ends clerical work and general fund-raising are the main jobs for volunteers.

VOLUNTEERS REQUIRED
Volunteers of all age groups are welcome and no specific qualifications are necessary, though general office experience would be an asset.

TRAINING
Volunteers are given training.

HOURS
Hours are by agreement but principally between 9 a.m. and 5.30 p.m.

CONTACT
Contact the General Secretary at the above address.

Note: See The Blood Transfusion Service Board, entry No. 12.

58   IRISH HEART FOUNDATION

4 Clyde Road, Ballsbridge, Dublin 4. (01) 685001

NATURE OF WORK
The IHF aims to reduce mortality and disability from Cardio Vascular Disease and stroke in Ireland by Research, Education and Community Service (Blood Pressure Clinics, Lectures, Screening etc.).

VOLUNTEERS REQUIRED
No special qualifications are necessary and volunteers over 18 years are needed to help promote the aims of the Foundation and for fund-raising.

TRAINING
Suitable training is provided for the work undertaken.

HOURS
Volunteers are normally required for just one activity a year.

CONTACT
Contact the Director of the Head Office as above or the Cork Office at 41 Mac Curtain Street, Cork.

59   IRISH LUPUS SUPPORT GROUP LTD.

40 Killester Park, Dublin 5. (01) 318524/453317

NATURE OF WORK
A voluntary organisation which aims to be a source of contact and mutual support to fellow sufferers of Lupus (Systemic Lupus Erythematosus or SLE). The group has a programme of information and education to help Lupus sufferers and their families come to terms with this disease and all that it entails.

VOLUNTEERS REQUIRED
Lupus sufferers, their families and friends are all welcome. Secretarial work, compilation of newsletter

and day to day running of the group are all carried out on a voluntary basis and funded solely by voluntary donations.

TRAINING
The group avails of training courses organised by the National Social Services Board. There are also regular Support and Educational meetings for members with Consultant Doctors in attendance.

HOURS
Volunteers work by arrangement or as required.

CONTACT
Mrs. Catherine Delaney, Hon. Secretary, at the above address. The group has active branches in Cork and Tralee and hopes to establish regional branches throughout Ireland.

60   IRISH MISSIONARY UNION

Orwell Park, Rathgar, Dublin 6. (01) 965433

NATURE OF WORK
The IMU is a co-ordinating body for all Mission Sending Organisations, both laity and religious. Within the IMU is a Laity Department which is involved in the recruitment, selection and training of laity for missions.

VOLUNTEERS REQUIRED
Volunteers must be over 21 years and have a professional qualification or skill in such areas as Medical, Trades, Education, Agriculture or Pastoral.

TRAINING
Volunteers attend a 9-day residential course.

CONTACT
The Laity Officer, IMU, at the above address.

61 IRISH MOTOR NEURONE DISEASE ASSOCIATION

Community Services Headquarters,
13 Christchurch Place, Dublin 8. (01) 540921

NATURE OF WORK
Helping sufferers and their families with information, counselling, supplying aids and visitation, and raising funds for the provision of a support service and for research.

VOLUNTEERS REQUIRED
No particular qualifications are necessary but volunteers should be reasonably mature.

TRAINING
No training is provided at present.

HOURS
Volunteers by arrangement in their own time.

CONTACT
The Irish Association is anxious to increase its branch network throughout Ireland and anyone wishing to join or interested in forming a local branch should contact the above address for full details.

62   IRISH RED CROSS SOCIETY

16 Merrion Square, Dublin 2. (01) 765135

NATURE OF WORK
Humanitarian Work – Ambulance Service, First-Aid Courses, Care of Refugees, Youth Red Cross Group, Community Services.

VOLUNTEERS REQUIRED
All age groups are welcome to join. The Red Cross encourages the participation of young people and provides youth programmes and opportunities for youth to participate in international friendship events organised by the Red Cross at home and abroad.

TRAINING
All members receive initial and on-going training.

HOURS
Hours depend on what group the volunteer joins.

CONTACT
There are several branches of the Irish Red Cross Society throughout Ireland and full details are available from the above address. For Youth Work contact Ms Juanita Majury, Youth Director, and all other enquiries to The General Secretary.

63   IRISH SOCIETY FOR AUTISTIC CHILDREN

14 Lower O'Connell Street, Dublin 1. (01) 742783

NATURE OF WORK
Working with young Autistic adults in a community setting, social training, etc., and organising fund-raising projects and Autism Awareness projects.

VOLUNTEERS REQUIRED
Volunteers should be over 18 years. There are no qualification requirements but there is a need for patience and a definite commitment.

TRAINING
Training is given to volunteers if required.

HOURS
There are no specific hours but individuals are required to give a regular commitment.

CONTACT
Mrs. Nuala Matthews at the above address, or the Dunfirth Community for Persons with Autism, Johnstown Bridge, Enfield, Co. Kildare.

64   IRISH SOCIETY FOR COLITIS AND CROHN'S DISEASE

204 Limekiln Farm, Dublin 12.

NATURE OF WORK
A group of sufferers, their families and friends, working to raise funds for research and to keep members and the public informed on these chronic diseases.

CONTACT
For information on the diseases or the Society meeting times etc. contact Colette Murphy, Hon. Secretary, at the above address.

65   IRISH SOCIETY FOR THE PREVENTION OF CRUELTY TO ANIMALS

1 Grand Canal Quay, Dublin 1. (01) 775922

NATURE OF WORK
This voluntary organisation is a registered charity with a branch in every county of Ireland and aims to prevent as far as possible cruelty to animals through education and advice. The society provides a 24-acre farm at Liscarrol, Co. Cork for the rehabilitation of sick and/or disabled horses, free farrier schemes in several country areas to pare donkeys' hooves, etc. and animal dispensaries.

VOLUNTEERS REQUIRED
All members are volunteers and anyone with an interest in animal welfare welcome.

TRAINING
No training is provided or necessary.

HOURS
Hours are varied and voluntary.

CONTACT
Contact Hon. Secretary of the local branch or the Head Office as above.

66 IRISH SOCIETY FOR THE PREVENTION OF CRUELTY TO CHILDREN

20 Molesworth Street, Dublin 2. (01) 760423/4/5

NATURE OF WORK
A voluntary child protection agency providing Family Support Services, Family Centres, Preschools and Childline Service for children in trouble or danger (phone 793333).

VOLUNTEERS REQUIRED
All age groups are welcome; particularly volunteers who have worked with children.

TRAINING
Childline counsellors undergo full training course.

HOURS
Childline counsellors work 4 – 8 hours per week. Fundraising and other activities by arrangement or when required.

CONTACT
Cian O'Tighearnaigh or Rosemary Troy at the above address.

67 IRISH WHEELCHAIR ASSOCIATION

Blackheath Drive, Clontarf, Dublin 3.
(01) 338241/2/3 333860

NATURE OF WORK
Voluntary social service agency working with and on behalf of wheelchair users to improve their quality of life through direct service provision, encouraging improvements in community supports and services and by increasing community education/awareness.

VOLUNTEERS REQUIRED
Volunteers of any age group and no particular qualifications are required for driving, visiting, organising social activities and holidays, fund-raising, lobbying for change, and creating community awareness.

TRAINING
There is a General Induction Training for new volunteers under the headings The Voluntary Driver, The Voluntary Visitor or The Holiday Helper.

HOURS
Hours vary and people can usually pick times that suit them.

CONTACT
There are over 50 branches throughout Ireland and details are available from the national Headquarters above or the following Regional Offices:

Galway Road, Kinnegad, Co. Westmeath. (044) 753456
Parnell Street, Kilkenny. (056) 62775
Hession Buildings, 35/37 Dominick Street, Galway. (091) 65598
Main Street, Bundoran, Co. Donegal. (072) 41765
Sawmill Street, Cork. (021) 966350
Limerick Social Service Centre, Henry Street, Limerick. (061) 313691

68 JOMAC

119 Homefarm Road, Drumcondra, Dublin 9.
(01) 360174

NATURE OF WORK
To entertain the sick, senior citizens, deserving children, etc.

VOLUNTEERS REQUIRED
Vacancies arise occasionally for young musicians, dancers, singers, etc.

TRAINING
Experience is not necessary, but a talent will be encouraged at rehearsals and performances.

HOURS
Season runs from September to May and involves about two evenings per week.

CONTACT
Jomac hold an annual fund-raising show in the St. Francis Xavier Hall, Dublin, in April/May for which support is always valued and this and all other functions are advertised in newspapers. For full details write to the Hon. Secretary at the above address or phone 360174 evenings only.

69 THE MARRIAGE COUNSELLING SERVICE

24 Grafton Street, Dublin 2. (01) 720341

NATURE OF WORK
Marital and relationship counselling and providing talks to schools and groups and other voluntary services.

VOLUNTEERS REQUIRED
Volunteers are required as receptionists, preferably mature people with an interest in the area of the Service. The counsellors are professionally trained, caring men and women who voluntarily give of their time to the Marriage Counselling Service.

TRAINING
Volunteers are introduced to the routine involved in reception work. Counsellors undergo a rigorous selection process and ongoing comprehensive training.

HOURS
Receptionists are required Monday to Friday 4 p.m. to 10 p.m. and work by arrangement within these hours. Counsellors work Monday to Friday 10 a.m. to 9 p.m., each giving three counselling hours per week.

CONTACT
Write to the Secretary at the above address or phone 720341 between 9.30 a.m. and 2 p.m.

70   M.E.(MYALGIC ENCEPHALOMYELITIS) ASSOCIATION

c/o 80 Foxfield Road, Raheny, Dublin 5.

NATURE OF WORK
M.E. is an extremely variable physical illness which results from *not* recovering from a virus infection. The Association is a self-help support group for sufferers and their relatives which aims to promote awareness of the disease among the public and the medical profession and to support research.

CONTACT
Write to Miriam Sheridan at the above address.

71 MUSCULAR DYSTROPHY IRELAND

29 Eaton Square, Monkstown, Co. Dublin.
(01) 802870

NATURE OF WORK
Muscular Dystrophy is primarily a wasting disease affecting all voluntary muscles and there are many different types for which, at present, there is no cure or treatment. The Association is involved in promoting research, supporting families, and organising fund-raising events (all funds raised are used to support medical research).

VOLUNTEERS REQUIRED
Volunteers of any age group are welcome, persons with secretarial skills, nursing or social work training, or interested in helping with fund-raising i.e. interested in assisting with the organisation of events or willing to participate in sponsored events, marathons, fun runs, etc.

TRAINING
On the job training is provided for nurses/social workers.

HOURS
Hours are by arrangement.

CONTACT
Derek Farrell at the above address.

72   NARCOTICS ANONYMOUS

P.O. Box 1368 Sheriff Street, Dublin 1.
(01) 300944 ext 486

NATURE OF WORK
A fellowship of men and women who help each other to
recover from addiction through a self-help programme.

CONTACT
Details of the Organisation and meeting times and
venues are available from the Irish Service Office of N.A.
at 13 Talbot Street, Dublin 1.

73   NATIONAL ADULT
LITERACY AGENCY

8 Gardiner Place, Dublin 1. (01) 787205

NATURE OF WORK
NALA is a national Referral Agency for literacy students
and tutors, offering help and advice on organisation,
training tutors, resources and materials; building
regional and local networks of support and development; organising meetings, seminars and workshops.

VOLUNTEERS REQUIRED
Volunteer tutors should be mature adults and prepared
to commit themselves to twelve months work with the
scheme. No qualifications are required but they should
relate well to other adults and be able to show sensitivity
to the needs of adults with literacy difficulties.

TRAINING

The NALA does not run initial tutor-training courses but will refer volunteers to their local literacy scheme where training usually involves one evening a week for six to nine weeks with continuing back-up.

HOURS

Literacy tutors usually work on a one-to-one basis and are expected to spend two hours a week with the student plus preparation time.

CONTACT

There are about forty Literacy Schemes throughout Ireland and details are available from the National Adult Literacy Agency as above or direct from your local scheme.

74 NATIONAL COUNCIL FOR THE BLIND OF IRELAND

45 Whitworth Road, Dublin 9. (01) 307033

NATURE OF WORK

The N.C.B.I. provides social services and information to people who are visually impaired.

VOLUNTEERS REQUIRED

Volunteers in the 30-65 age group are required as readers to read onto tape for visually-impaired people. As readers will, in some cases, be reading professional books they should be proficient in a given subject.

TRAINING
Training is provided for volunteers.

HOURS
Essentially people read in their own time, giving them flexibility.

CONTACT
Contact the Librarian at the Head Office as above, or Mrs. Joan Murphy at the Branch office, White Street, Cork. (021) 962836

75   NATIONAL ECZEMA SOCIETY

Tavistock House North, Tavistock Square,
London WC1H 9SR

NATURE OF WORK
An organisation offering support and information for families of eczema sufferers.

CONTACT
Irish contacts can be reached by phone at (01) 892343 or (01) 557807.

76 NATIONAL FEDERATION OF ARCH CLUBS

74 Meadow Grove, Dublin 14. (01) 951081

NATURE OF WORK
Providing recreational facilities for persons with a mental handicap. Furthering the process of normalisation and acceptance into society of persons with a mental handicap. Educating society to accept the mentally handicapped in their midst.

VOLUNTEERS REQUIRED
Each club is autonomous and the age group and volunteer requirements vary from one club to another.

TRAINING
Four or five committed people, who are willing to come together and to organise, should be sufficient to start a club and assistance and advice are provided by the National Federation.

HOURS
Depend on individual club-based activities.

CONTACT
There are at present over thirty clubs in Counties Dublin, Kildare, Kilkenny, Louth, Mayo and Meath. Full details are available from the General Secretary, National Federation of Arch Clubs, 74 Meadow Grove, Dublin 14.

77 NATIONAL SOCIAL SERVICE BOARD

71 Lower Leeson Street, Dublin 2. (01) 616422

NATURE OF WORK

The NSSB is a statutory body promoting public information on and accessibility of social services and is the central registering body for local voluntary Community Information Centres. The Board runs training courses for voluntary workers and provides advice and assistance to voluntary groups on training, insurance and other matters. It may also assist new national voluntary organisations to set up and operates a library of audio-visual aids for voluntary groups.

78 NATIONAL YOUTH COUNCIL OF IRELAND

3 Montague Street, Dublin 2. (01) 784122

NATURE OF WORK

Co-ordinating body of voluntary youth organisations in Ireland, comprising 43 organisations including cultural, political, youth clubs, scouts, guides, etc.

VOLUNTEERS REQUIRED

Volunteers are nominated by NYCI's member organisations to work on various issue areas being considered by the Council.

TRAINING
NYCI organises briefing sessions for new volunteers.

CONTACT
Information and list of member organisations available from the above address.

79 ORDER OF MALTA AMBULANCE CORPS

St John's House, 32 Clyde Road, Ballsbridge, Dublin 4. (01) 684891

NATURE OF WORK
'Caring for the Community'. This is achieved through Ambulance Services and First Aid, Community Care Work and Youth Work.

VOLUNTEERS REQUIRED
In order to join volunteers must complete a course in first aid of six weeks duration and must be 16 years or over. No matter how much or how little time volunteers have to spare the Ambulance Corps needs their technical skills, business ability or support in any capacity to continue and expand their community services in Ireland.

TRAINING
Volunteers are trained in all aspects of first aid, home nursing, leadership and youth work.

HOURS
Volunteers attend a weekly meeting and carry out duties as their time allows.

CONTACT
Order of Malta Ambulance Corps units are active in some 120 communities in the Republic and Northern Ireland. For membership details and further information contact the Ambulance Corps at the above address.

80 ORDER OF MALTA CADET CORPS

St John's House, 32 Clyde Road, Ballsbridge, Dublin 4. (01) 684891

NATURE OF WORK
The Order of Malta Cadet Corps (junior section of the Order of Malta Ambulance Corps) is a voluntary national youth organisation providing development opportunities for young people. The Order of Malta Cadet Corps aims to develop its youth spiritually, mentally and physically by encouraging the spirit of adventure and service.

VOLUNTEERS REQUIRED
The Cadet Units are for boys and girls between the ages of 10 and 16 years. At 16 years cadets may join the Ambulance Corps.

TRAINING

The Cadet Corps provides training in first aid and operates a Cadet Proficiency Scheme offering some 85 programme activities. An award system has been built into the scheme. Each project completed is assessed and a Certificate of Proficiency awarded to those who meet the required standard together with a series of special badges.

HOURS

Cadets meet weekly to train and practice.

CONTACT

The Cadet Corps is organised in some 80 unit areas throughout the Republic and Northern Ireland and full information is available from the above address.

81   OXFAM IN IRELAND

202 Lr Rathmines Road, Dublin 6.
(01) 972195/966792

NATURE OF WORK

Third World Development Agency.

VOLUNTEERS REQUIRED

Volunteers are required for shop work, fund-raising and education work.

TRAINING

Training is provided for volunteers.

HOURS
Hours are by agreement depending on the work under-taken.

CONTACT
Contact the Oxfam Office at the above address.

82 PACE: PRISONERS AID THROUGH COMMUNITY EFFORT

7 Upper Leeson Street, Dublin 4.

NATURE OF WORK
Rehabilitation of Ex-Offenders.

VOLUNTEERS REQUIRED
Volunteers are required for fund-raising.

TRAINING
No training is required.

HOURS
Hours depend on the work undertaken.

CONTACT
Betty Clarke, Executive Secretary, at the above address. The organisation also runs a Hostel at Priorswood House, Coolock, Dublin 17 and a Workshop at Santry Hall Industrial Estate, Dublin 9.

83 PARENTS UNDER STRESS

Centre Care, Cathedral Street, Dublin 1.
(01) 742066/788344

NATURE OF WORK
Aid for Parents under Stress is a voluntary organisation offering a telephone helpline service to parents who are having difficulty in coping with their feelings and actions of aggression or rejection towards their children.

VOLUNTEERS REQUIRED
Volunteers are required to man the phones and are selected after an initial interview.

TRAINING
Initial and ongoing training is provided to enable volunteers to listen and help the caller talk out his/her feelings.

HOURS
Volunteers are required to work a minimum of 4 hours per week. At present the telephone hours are mornings afternoons and evenings and these are being extended as more volunteers become available.

CONTACT
Phone or write to Parents Under Stress at the above address.

84 POLIO FELLOWSHIP OF IRELAND

Park House, Stillorgan Grove, Stillorgan,
Co. Dublin. (01) 888366

NATURE OF WORK
The Polio Fellowship of Ireland was founded in 1952 with the primary aim of providing help and rehabilitation for those struck down by polio. The service has now been expanded to include a wider range of disability and to provide vocational training and day care services with a large range of activities.

VOLUNTEERS REQUIRED
Volunteers are needed to assist with clients in the Day Activity Centre and are also required for Committee work.

TRAINING
Training is provided as required.

HOURS
Hours are varied and depend on the work undertaken.

CONTACT
Mr. T. J. Stephens at the above address.

85 R.P. IRELAND –
FIGHTING BLINDNESS

8 North Great Georges Street, Dublin 1. (01) 746756

NATURE OF WORK
Retinitis Pigmentosa (R.P.) is the name given to a group of hereditary diseases of the Retina, the light sensitive tissue inside the eye. While independent, the Irish society is part of a worldwide movement to combat it, and concerns itself with fund-raising for research, acting as a focal point for sufferers, and educating the public about the special needs of sufferers.

VOLUNTEERS REQUIRED
Volunteers of all age groups are welcome and no qualifications are required. Primarily volunteers would be involved in fund-raising but would also be encouraged to join their local branch where the assistance of fully sighted people is always welcome.

TRAINING
Training is not usually required but on-the-job assistance is provided where necessary.

HOURS
Volunteers would normally be required to work in the evenings and at weekends.

CONTACT
The Society has a branch network throughout Ireland and details and all other information are available from the National Development Co-Ordinator at the above address.

86   THE RAPE CRISIS CENTRE

70 Lower Leeson Street, Dublin 2.
(01) 614911/913923

NATURE OF WORK
The Centre offers a 24-hour service to provide help, support, advice and information to girls, boys, men and women who have been sexually abused, and counselling and support for friends and relatives of those who have been sexually abused.

VOLUNTEERS REQUIRED
Men and women from age 16 upwards are required to help with flag day collecting, event planning and organising, such as designing, artwork, T-shirts, posters, etc., and for office administration.

TRAINING
Where necessary on the job training is provided.

HOURS
Volunteers work by arrangement for as much or as little time as they have available. The Centre depends on fund-raising and considers just 4 hours flag day collecting once a year a very valuable contribution.

CONTACT
Helen Shortall at the above address or the following Rape Crisis Centres:
P.O. Box 46, Belfast BT 7AR. (084) 249696
c/o Community Care Centre, 3 Wellington St.,
    Clonmel. (052) 24111

P.O. Box 42, Brian Boru Street, Cork. (021) 968086
15 Mary Street, Galway. (091) 64983
P.O. Box 128, Limerick.

87 REFUGEE RESETTLEMENT COMMITTEE

29 Lower Baggot Street, Dublin 2.
(01) 785455/785005

NATURE OF WORK
Resettlement of refugees into Irish society. Some of the main functions of the organisation include counselling, organising English language training, housing and employment.

VOLUNTEERS REQUIRED
Volunteers aged 20 and upwards are required to teach English, and of any age to give community support.

TRAINING
Volunteers are provided with general background information.

HOURS
Volunteers would be required to work on a part-time basis. The number of hours would be negotiable.

CONTACT
Full details from the above address.

88 RETIREMENT PLANNING COUNCIL OF IRELAND

16 Harcourt Street, Dublin 2. (01) 783600

NATURE OF WORK

The Retirement Planning Council of Ireland is a voluntary body which provides education for those approaching retirement by creating awareness of the problems of retirement, helping to set up local pre-retirement associations, and establishing ways to allow the energies, skills, knowledge and experience of retired people to be used for their own good and that of the community.

The Council has recently set up a Volunteer Placement Service for persons approaching, or in retirement, who are interested in doing some voluntary work and aims to place volunteers in organisations which seek them. At present the scheme seeks volunteers from the pre-retirement courses run by the Council, but is willing to assist any reader who is interested in working for an organisation but hesitant about making the first approach. There is no charge for this service either to the individual or the organisation.

Further information on the Volunteer Placement Scheme and all aspects of the work of the Council are available from Mr. Hilary Shannon, Chief Executive, at the above address.

89   ROYAL NATIONAL LIFEBOAT INSTITUTION

3 Clare Street, Dublin 2. (01) 762217

NATURE OF WORK
The preservation of life from ship-wreck.

VOLUNTEERS REQUIRED
Competent seamen in the immediate area of the life-boat stations and volunteers to assist with fund-raising.

TRAINING
Relevant training is provided where necessary.

HOURS
Life-boat crews are on call round the clock; volunteers for fund-raising work by arrangement when required.

CONTACT
Full details from the above address or contact local branch.

90   RUBENSTEIN-TAYBI SYNDROME SUPPORT GROUP

c/o 54 Knocklyon Green, Knocklyon Woods, Templeogue, Dublin 16. (01) 941169/288661

NATURE OF WORK
R.T.S. was first described in 1963 by Drs. Rubenstein and Taybi to cover a group of abnormal findings including

mental and motor retardation in young children. The Group is a support group for parents of RTS children offering advice, support and information on research.

CONTACT
Mrs. Linda Fair, Chairperson, at the above address.

91 THE SALLYNOGGIN OLD FOLKS ASSOCIATION

The Social Centre for the Aged, Church Place, Sallynoggin, Dun Laoghaire, Co. Dublin.
(01) 851338

NATURE OF WORK
Providing amenities for the aged of the Sallynoggin community.

VOLUNTEERS REQUIRED
Volunteers of any active age are welcome, with an outlook of dedication to the welfare of the aged.

TRAINING
No training is required.

HOURS
Volunteers are required mostly in the evenings to assist with Old Folk Socials, Fund-raising Bingo and similar functions.

CONTACT
John J. Hoare P.C. or Rita O'Brien at the Social Centre as above, or phone Mr. Hoare at 801018 during business hours or at 851257 at home.

92   THE SAMARITANS

112 Marlborough Street, Dublin 1. (01) 727700

NATURE OF WORK
A 24-hour telephone service for the lonely, despairing, anxious or suicidal person, or for anyone who feels it would help to have someone to talk to. Samaritan centres are open to personal callers between 10 a.m. and 9.30 p.m. and letters are also welcome.

VOLUNTEERS REQUIRED
No particular qualifications are necessary but volunteers must be over 19 and would require an ability to listen to callers who may need to share painful feelings with them.

TRAINING
Prospective volunteers have an initial interview and preparation course followed by a further interview and six month trial period.

HOURS
Volunteers are required to work four hours a week every week, and to take an overnight duty in the centre once every six weeks and a week-end duty every two months.

CONTACT
Write to the Director of your local branch. Republic branches are as follows:

Dublin: 112 Marlborough Street, Dublin 1. (01) 727700
Cork: Coach Street, Cork. (021) 271323
Ennis: Kilrush Road, Ennis. (065) 29777
Limerick: 25 Upper Cecil Street, Limerick. (061) 42111
Sligo: 12 Chapel Street, Sligo. (071) 42011
Waterford: 13 Beau Street, Waterford. (051) 72114

93   SAOL PLUS

8 Park Road, off Navan Road, Dublin 7. (01) 382475

NATURE OF WORK
Giving instruction in sport and physical activities to people of all ages who do not normally take part in such activities.

VOLUNTEERS REQUIRED
Persons aged 18 and upwards are required to train as certified instructors in particular sports and activities.

TRAINING
Appropriate training is given to volunteer instructors.

HOURS
Anytime! Evening sessions, seminars, weekend courses, international courses and holidays are arranged by Saol Plus.

CONTACT
Paula Bermingham, Secretary, at the above address.

94 SCHIZOPHRENIA ASSOCIATION OF IRELAND

4 Fitzwilliam Place, Dublin 2. (01) 761988

NATURE OF WORK
A self-help mutual support organisation for families of persons affected by Schizophrenia, offering advice, support and counselling to members, and aiming in the long term to provide relief to sufferers and alleviation of distress amongst their families through research, promotion and education.

VOLUNTEERS REQUIRED
Volunteers are required as Branch leaders and officials, for committee work at National and Local level, and for fund-raising. The Association welcomes anyone who is interested in the disease or a relative or friend of a sufferer, but in particular those with specialised training, e.g. social skills, medical qualifications, or community care experience.

TRAINING
No formal training is provided but representatives from each branch meet regularly for work-days.

HOURS
Hours vary between branches and depend on the fund-raising project or work being undertaken.

CONTACT
The Schizophrenia Association has a network of some 18 branches throughout the country and full details are available from the Head Office as above.

95 SEPARATED PERSONS ASSOCIATION

10 Blessington Street, Dublin 7. (01) 381101

NATURE OF WORK
A self-support group for separated people to help each other to cope with everyday life after separation.

CONTACT
Details of meetings, venues and times in Dublin and Cork are available from the above address.

96 SIMON COMMUNITY

P.O. Box 1022, Lr Sheriff Street, Dublin 1.
(01) 711606/711319

NATURE OF WORK
Simon runs night shelters, residential houses, soup-runs, out-reach and follow-up services for homeless people in Cork, Dublin, Dundalk and Galway.

VOLUNTEERS REQUIRED
Volunteers aged 18 and over are required either on a full-time basis to live and work in Simon shelters and houses for a minimum period of three months, or part-time to commit themselves to one evening a week working in a Simon project.

TRAINING
Training is ongoing and involves introductory days, seminars, conferences, workshops and publications.

HOURS
Full-time volunteers live and work in Simon projects.
They operate on a rota basis which is usually 3/4 days on
and 2 days off. Part-time volunteers are usually required
in the evening time.

CONTACT
Those interested in full-time voluntary work should
contact the Assistant National Director at the National
Office as above. Those interested in part-time work
should contact their local Community as follows:

Cork: P.O. Box 76, Brian Boru St., Cork. (021) 277516
Dublin: P.O. Box 581, Dublin 1. (01) 720188
Dundalk: Sunnyside House, Barrack Street,
Dundalk. (042) 35211
Galway: P.O. Box 5, Galway. (091) 64962

97   SOCIETY OF ST. VINCENT DE PAUL

8 New Cabra Road, Dublin 7. (01) 384164

NATURE OF WORK
The Society of St Vincent de Paul is an international lay
organisation which seeks, in a spirit of justice and
charity, to help all who are in need, through services
which include Family Visitation, Holiday Homes,
Housing for the Homeless and the Elderly, Hospital
Visitation, Day Centres, Clothing Shops, Youth Clubs,
Seamen's Clubs, 'Half-way House' facilities for unmar-
ried mothers and Child Care.

VOLUNTEERS REQUIRED
All volunteers who are willing to give of their time to helping others are welcome.

TRAINING
Training is provided where necessary.

HOURS
Volunteers are required to attend a weekly meeting which would last for about 2 hours and to visit families which would take about another 2 hours.

CONTACT
The Society has over 900 branches in Ireland and contact can be made direct to the local branch or to the Society's offices at:
8 New Cabra Road, Dublin 7.
2 Tuckey Street, Cork.
Ozanam House, Augustine Street, Galway.
Ozanam House, Hartstonge Street, Limerick.
224 Antrim Road, Belfast.

98   THE ST. JOHN'S AMBULANCE BRIGADE OF IRELAND

29 Upper Leeson Street, Dublin 2. (01) 688077

NATURE OF WORK
To give first aid to those stricken ill suddenly in public places.

VOLUNTEERS REQUIRED

Men, women and cadets are required to assist in the stated function of the Ambulance Brigade and to raise funds necessary to maintain the training programmes and to provide equipment, bandages, etc.

TRAINING

All members must be trained in first-aid and home nursing.

HOURS

Hours are by arrangement and depend on the work undertaken.

CONTACT

The National Headquarters at the above address.

99   TEL-A-FRIEND

10 Fownes Street, Dublin 2. (01) 777847/719379

NATURE OF WORK

Confidential information and befriending service offering counselling in gay sexuality and sexual identity.

VOLUNTEERS REQUIRED

Volunteers are carefully chosen as receptive and understanding people who are easy to talk to and willing to offer friendship and support to others. T.A.F. workers are gay.

TRAINING

Extensive training is provided and back-up services are

available from specialists such as doctors, priests, solicitors and others.

HOURS
Volunteers are required to work for a minimum of two hours a week.

CONTACT
The Director at the above address.

100   THRESHOLD LIMITED

Church Street, Dublin 7. (01) 720769

NATURE OF WORK
Threshold is a national voluntary housing advice and research service offering advice and help to people with housing problems, mainly in the Private Rented sector.

VOLUNTEERS REQUIRED
Volunteers are required to assist the staff in helping callers and experience in Legal/Social work would be an advantage.

TRAINING
Full training is available.

HOURS
Volunteers work by arrangement during the opening hours, 9.30 a.m. to 5.30 p.m. and 6.00 to 8.00 p.m. on Tuesdays (Late Opening Rathmines 6.00 to 8.00 p.m. on Thursdays).

Mr. Barry O'Hagan, National Director, at the National Office above or any branch office as follows:
52 Lr. Rathmines Road, Dublin 6.
8 Fr. Matthew Quay, Cork.
Ozanam House, St. Augustine St., Galway.

101 TURNING POINT

2 Lansdowne Gardens, Shelbourne Road, Ballsbridge, Dublin 4. (01) 602600

NATURE OF WORK
Support, counselling, relaxation and diet for those in life crisis especially bereavement and life-threatening illnesses such as cancer.

VOLUNTEERS REQUIRED
Volunteers of any age are welcome and are required most importantly for fund-raising and also for driving clients to and from the centre, gardening and secretarial duties.

TRAINING
Very little training is required but orientation to the centre's work is provided.

HOURS
Hours are flexible.

CONTACT
Kay Conroy or Mary-Paula Walsh at the above address.

102 UNICEF (U.N. CHILDREN'S FUND) IRISH NATIONAL COMMITTEE

4 St Andrew Street, Dublin 2. (01) 770843

NATURE OF WORK
Voluntary charitable organisation.

VOLUNTEERS REQUIRED
Adults with energy and common sense are required for office or shop work.

TRAINING
Training is available if needed.

HOURS
Volunteers can choose their own time and duration during business hours, 9.30 a.m. to 5.30 p.m.

CONTACT
Dorothy Archer, Executive Director, at the above address.

103 VIATORES CHRISTI

36/39 Gardiner Street, Dublin 1.
(01) 728027/749346

NATURE OF WORK
Viatores Christi means Travellers for Christ. It is a lay missionary association dedicated to the active involve-

ment of Catholic laity in the missionary work of the Church, including recruitment, training, placing overseas, and re-entry on return.

VOLUNTEERS REQUIRED
Volunteers for overseas must be over 21 with a strong desire to share in a mission project. Volunteers are also required on the home front for fund-raising, etc.

TRAINING
Volunteers are invited to take part in the training programme organised by Viatores Christi before being interviewed for an overseas assignment.

HOURS
Overseas assignments are normally for two years and renewable. Home-based volunteers work by individual arrangement.

CONTACT
The Secretary at the above address.

104 VOLUNTARY SERVICE INTERNATIONAL

4/5 Eustace Street, Dublin 2. (01) 719067

NATURE OF WORK
VSI is part of an international movement working for peace and international understanding through the medium of practical voluntary work and international exchanges, including renovating flats for elderly people,

childrens outings, work with the handicapped, environmental work and Third World work.

VOLUNTEERS REQUIRED
Volunteers must be over 17 for work in Ireland, over 18 for Europe and over 21 for Asia and Africa.

TRAINING
There is a series of internal training for members.

HOURS
Local groups work a minimum of 5/6 hours each week; International Workcamps are usually for two to three weeks; Asia/Africa camps usual period two to three months; Volunteers in Africa minimum period two years.

CONTACT
The Secretary at the above address.

105 THE VOLUNTEER STROKE SCHEME

249 Crumlin Road, Dublin 12. (01) 557455

NATURE OF WORK
A voluntary organisation to help people who suffer from speech and allied problems as a result of a stroke, by offering volunteers to visit the patient, a club where patients can meet and be helped, and outings from time to time, and by creating a greater awareness and understanding of Stroke.

VOLUNTEERS REQUIRED
Male and female volunteers aged 18 years upwards are required.

TRAINING
Basic training is provided.

HOURS
Volunteers are required to visit patients for one hour weekly.

CONTACT
Contact the Volunteer Stroke Scheme at the above address.